MICKEY MOUSE CLUBHOUSE

THE SCAVENGER HUNT

Advance
PUBLISHERS

Advance Publishers, L.C.
1060 Maitland Center Commons, Suite 365
Maitland, FL 32751 USA

10 9 8 7 6 5 4 3 2 1
ISBN-10: 1-57973-387-5

Mickey and his pals had a fun day planned. They were going on a scavenger hunt. They needed to find each thing on their list: a raccoon, a penguin, a sea star, and a rattlesnake.

There are pink and purple flowers in the Clubhouse.

FLOWERS

Flowers are plants. You can hold a flower by its long stem. Leaves come out from the stem. And at the top, there are many colorful petals.

The friends started by looking for the rattlesnake in the Clubhouse.

"It's not in the cupboard," said Minnie.

"It's not in the flowerpot," said Donald.

Daisy shrugged. "I don't see it anywhere inside the Clubhouse."

"Me either," said Mickey. "I think we're going to need some special Mouseketools so we'll know where to look for the things on our list. Everyone say, 'Oh, Toodles!'"

DOGS

Some dogs live with city families. Some dogs live with country families. This dog is a pet. But there are hunting dogs, police dogs, herd dogs, and fire dogs. Dogs can do many jobs!

Mickey wonders what they'll find with the trees Mouseketool.

TREES

Trees are the tallest plants. The big, middle part of a tree is the trunk. Trees also have branches that spread out from the trunk. And leaves wave to you from the ends of the branches!

Toodles flew in with the Mouseketools: a cactus, trees, waves, and a Mystery Mouseketool. The Mystery Mouseketool is a surprise tool that could help them when they need it.

"Oh, boy, our Mouseketools are here!" said Mickey. "Now, which one will help us locate a rattlesnake?"

"I've never seen a rattlesnake at the beach, so I don't think the waves will help us," said Minnie.

"How about the cactuses?" asked Daisy. "They are found in deserts."

"Good idea," said Mickey. "We've got ears! Say cheers!"

Daisy knows her cactuses.

CACTUSES

This beavertail cactus has beautiful pink flowers. A cactus is a plant that grows in the desert. Most cactuses are found in North American deserts.

Mickey doesn't want to climb this plant!

SAGURO

It is the biggest type of cactus plant. It can grow 75 feet high. That is as high as a seven-story building.

Everyone piled into the Toon Car and they drove off. Before long, Mickey stopped the car when he saw a cactus. They had found the desert!

"Golly, look how big this cactus is!" said Mickey.

"And look how cute these geckos are," said Minnie.

"Now we just need to find a rattlesnake," Mickey said.

Welcome to the world, baby gecko!

GECKOS

This little gecko is hatching from its egg! It grew inside its egg for six months. Now it looks just like its mommy.

Beware of the rattle.

SIDEWINDERS

Can you see the rattle on the end of that sidewinder's tail? The sidewinder Is part of the rattlesnake family. If it feels threatened, it shakes its tail as a warning.

Everyone looked for the rattlesnake. Goofy spotted it by a rock. "There it is!"
"Good job!" said Mickey.
"My, it's hot out here," said Minnie.

WELCOME TO THE DRY DESERT

My what big ears you have!

RABBITS

Rabbits live in many places. This one has come out of its burrow under the ground to look for food.

In fact, it was so hot, the friends quickly got back in the car. Everyone was happy to have found the first thing on the list, but it was time to visit a much cooler place!

An ice cold home.

HARP SEALS

Harp seals live on the ice. But they are not cold. They have a lot of fat under their skin. The fat helps keep them warm.

"What's next on our scavenger hunt list?" Mickey asked Donald.

"A penguin," replied Donald. "How about a Mouseketool to help us figure out where to find one?"

"Super idea," said Mickey. "Everyone say, 'Oh, Toodles!'"

Mickey looked at the remaining tools. It was time to use the Mystery Mouseketool: a seal.

"We've got ears! Say cheers!" said Mickey. "Let's go to where we'd find a seal—the South Pole."

"Oh, goody goody! Maybe we'll find a penguin there!" said Daisy.

Brrr...

POLES

Where are the two coldest places in the world? The North Pole and the South Pole. They are both so cold that most of the water there has frozen and turned to ice.

Goofy is excited to see a real seal.

SEALS

When seals swim under the frozen sea, they chew the ice above their heads. This makes a hole so they can pop their heads out to breathe.

"I see a seal," said Goofy. "Actually I see five seals! They sure are cute."

"Great!" Mickey yelled from the car. "That means we must be at the South Pole!"

Pluto leaped out of the car to see the friendly penguins.

"Oh, boy! Penguins! Another thing we found on our scavenger hunt list," said Donald. "That's two things, so far."

PENGUINS

What is black and white and waddles all over? A penguin! You can see thousands of penguins diving into the cold, cold water, at the South Pole.

ROOKERY

A group of penguins living together is called a rookery. Living side by side with many other penguins allows them to huddle together and stay warm.

"Gawrsh! It sure is cold at the South Pole!" Goofy said with a shiver.

Everyone readily agreed. The penguins and seals were very nice, but it was just too cold!

Quickly, Toodles was called, and the pals tried to figure out where they could find the next thing on their list: a raccoon. They chose the Mouseketool that was a few trees.

"We've got ears! Say cheers!" said Mickey.

Welcome to ANTARCTICA

Donald pointed to the signpost. "The forest is that way. Let's go—before we f-f-freeze!"

SANDY BEACH 1111 miles

COOL FOREST 1110 miles

Go, penguins, go!

SWIMMERS

Penguins are excellent swimmers, but they cannot fly. They use their flippers to paddle through the water and to keep their balance when waddling across slippery surfaces such as wet rocks or ice.

FORESTS

The Siberian taiga is the largest forest in the world. It spreads across northern Russia, and is as wide as the Atlantic Ocean!

They drove out of the cold and into the forest. "Look! There's a bunny," said, Daisy, Goofy, and Mickey all at the same time.

"We need a raccoon," said Donald.

"I see a raccoon!" Minnie suddenly said.

Welcome to the Cool FOREST

"Hot dog!" cheered Mickey. "Only one more thing to find: a sea star. Everyone say, 'Oh, Toodles!'"

"Which Mouseketool haven't we used yet?" asked Goofy.

"The waves!" said Daisy. "We find waves at the ocean."

"Super cheers! We've used all our Mouseketools!" said Mickey. "Let's go. It'll be our last stop." He could tell that everyone was getting a bit tired of driving.

DRY DESERT 10 miles

SANDY BEACH 1 mile

These raccoons are just like the one the friends spotted.

RACCOONS

Even summer nights are busy times for some animals. These baby raccoons were born in the spring. Raccoons like to sleep during the day and go out at night. Now, these babies are old enough to go exploring with their mommy.

There is so much wildlife that lives in the ocean.

OCEANS

An ocean is a big, big body of water. Many plants and animals live deep down under the ocean. Big waves roll in and out, and splash upon the seashore.

After a long drive, the group reached the sandy shores of the ocean.

"Eureka!" exclaimed Mickey. "We made it!"

It seemed as if the sea creatures were happy to see visitors. A dolphin leaped out of the water, and a whale, sea gulls and a turtle came to welcome them too.

This dolphin is like an acrobat in the water.

SEA CREATURES

A sea creature is an animal that lives in or around the sea. Some sea creatures are mammals. Sea mammals cannot stay underwater all the time. They have to come up to the surface to breathe the air.

SEA STARS

Most sea stars live on the ocean floor. Some sea stars live near the shore in little pools of water called tide pools. You might even see a sea star when you are at the beach!

Donald and Daisy hopped out of the car and ran to the sand.

"Oh, boy! Oh, boy!" said Donald. "I found the last thing on our list: a sea star." He counted all the sea stars on the shore. There were nine.

"That's wonderful," said Daisy. "And look—ten crabs."

"Don't get too close," Donald warned Daisy. "Crabs can pinch with their claws."

Daisy kissed him on the cheek. "How nice of you to care."

"Aw, shucks," said Donald, grinning.

CRABS

Other sea creatures like crabs and lobsters have shells, long arms, or sharp claws and stay underwater most of the time.

Mickey and Minnie love playing in the sand.

SAND

Sand is actually tiny bits of rocks and seashells that have been worn down by wind and water. Sand feels rough and gritty between your fingers.

The rest of the group happily got out of the car and into the sun and surf. They were ready to relax after their long scavenger hunt.

"That was a great adventure," Mickey told Minnie. "But next time, let's have our scavenger hunt closer to home!"

Minnie giggled—and agreed.